WICKED LOVELY
DESERT TALES
CHALLENGE

STORY BY
MELISSA MARR

ART BY
XIAN NU STUDIO

HAMBURG // LONDON // LOS ANGELES // TOKYO

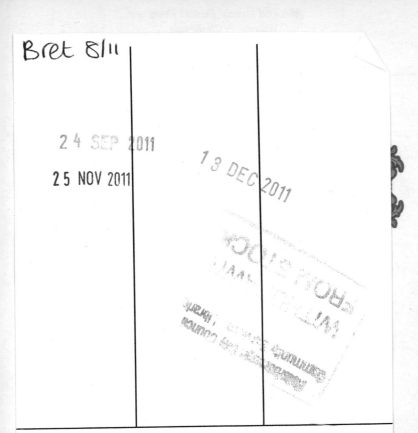

Bret 8/11

2 4 SEP 2011

2 5 NOV 2011

1 3 DEC 2011

PETERBOROUGH LIBRARIES

24 Hour renewal line 08458 505606

This book is to be returned on or before the latest date shown above, but may be renewed up to three times if the book is not in demand. Ask at your local library for details.

Please note that charges are made on overdue books

Wicked Lovely: Desert Tales
Volume 2: Challenge
Story by Melissa Marr
Art by Xian Nu Studio: Irene Diaz & Laura Moreno

Visual Storytelling Consultant - Barbara Randall Kesel

Lettering - John Hunt
Cover Design - Al-Insan Lashley

Senior Editor - Lillian Diaz-Przybyl
Pre-Production Supervisor - Vicente Rivera, Jr.
Pre-Production Specialist - Lucas Rivera
Managing Editor - Vy Nguyen
Senior Designer - Louis Csontos
Senior Designer - James Lee
Senior Editor - Bryce P. Coleman
Associate Publisher - Marco F. Pavia
President and C.O.O. - John Parker
C.E.O. and Chief Creative Officer - Stu Levy

A Manga

TOKYOPOP and are trademarks or registered trademarks of TOKYOPOP Inc.

TOKYOPOP Inc.
5900 Wilshire Blvd. Suite 2000
Los Angeles, CA 90036

E-mail: info@TOKYOPOP.com
Come visit us online at www.TOKYOPOP.com

SMART, ACTUALLY.

IT'S IRON, SHY.

RUSTY BITS OF POISON INSIDE YOUR BODY.

THEY'LL SEE YOU LIKE THIS, AN EXAMPLE OF WHAT HAPPENS WHEN I'M NOT OBEYED.

YOU'VE FORGOTTEN WHAT YOU ARE, AND I NEED YOU OUT OF MY WAY.

KAYLEY SHAMES *ME.*

I SWEAR I'M GOING TO TOP HER, AND SHE COMES OUT HARDER EVERY TIME.

WHY WAS KEENAN HERE?

HE WANTS ME TO BE HIS SUBJECT, SWEAR LOYALTY TO HIM.

IN EXCHANGE, HE'LL BACK ME IN CONTROLLING THE DESERT.

SO YOU'D BE LIKE...SORT OF LIKE A SHERIFF OR SOMETHING? LIKE IN CHARGE OF THEM?

YEAH, BUT I DON'T NEED HIM TO BE IN CHARGE. MIGHT AND WILL DETERMINE POWER OUT HERE.

REMIND THEM WHO'S IN CHARGE.

BUT YOU'RE STRONGER? WHY WAS HE IN CHARGE THEN?

IT FELT GOOD TOO. NOW I JUST NEED TO HOLD THINGS UNTIL SHY IS WELL, THEN HE CAN DEAL WITH A COUPLE DOZEN MOODY FAERIES.

SHY'S STRONG, AND I DIDN'T WANT TO BE INVOLVED. HE WAS HERE WHEN I GOT HERE...

I JUST WANTED TO DRAW AND BE ALONE.

NOW I JUST WANT TO DRAW AND BE ALONE WITH YOU.

YOU GET STUPIDER BY THE WEEK.

I TOLD SHY I'D NOT ATTACK YOU.

BUT DO YOU HONESTLY THINK I'LL FORGIVE THIS?

OF COURSE, SHY ISN'T TRUSTWORTHY EITHER.

BUT HE ISN'T TRYING TO STEAL EVERYONE'S FREEDOM.

Read on for a taste of
Melissa Marr's newest tale of Faerie,

RADIANT SHADOWS

Present day

Ani pulled open a side door to the stable. It was as much
a garage as a true stable, and as she walked through the
cavernous building she drew in the mingled scents of diesel
and straw, exhaust and sweat. Most of the creatures kept the
illusion of vehicles when they were outside the building, but
here, in their safe haven, the beasts roamed in whatever form
they chose. One of the steeds crouched on a ledge under
the skylight. It was something between an eagle and a lion;
both feathers and fur covered a massive body. Several other
steeds were lined up in a row of various motorcycles, cars,
and trucks. One anomalous steed was a camel.

A Hound looked up from polishing a matte black Harley
with plenty of chrome. The cloth in his hand was one of the
many swaths of fabric imported from Faerie specifically for
their steeds. "You looking for Chela?"

"No." She stayed in the walkway, not invading his space
or the steed's yet. "Not Chela."

Her father's semiregular mate was a source of comfort,
but Chela wanted to be more maternal than Ani could accept

from her. Similarly, her father's attempts at fatherhood veered toward something akin to mortal pretenses. She didn't want a facsimile of a mortal family. She had a family, with Rabbit and Tish, her half-mortal siblings. During the past year when she had been brought to live in the Dark Court, she had hoped for something else: she wanted to be a true part of the Wild Hunt, a full member of her father's pack. That hadn't happened.

The Hound paused his steady motions only long enough to glance at her. "Gabriel's not here either."

"I know. I'm not looking for anyone in particular." Ani came to the stall. "I just like it here."

The Hound looked up and down the open aisle. This early no other Hound was in sight, but there were more than a score of steeds close enough to see them. "Do you need something?"

"Sure." Ani leaned against the wall. It would be an insult not to flirt, even though they both knew action wasn't possible. "A little fun. A little trouble. A ride . . ."

"Get the boss to agree"—the Hound's eyes flashed a vibrant green—"and I'll gladly take you."

She knew her own eyes were shimmering with the same energy that she saw in his. They were both born of the Wild Hunt. They were the creatures that rode the earth, drawing out terror, exacting vengeance, unrestrained by order. They were the teeth and claws of Faerie, living now in the mortal world, bound to the Dark Court by their Gabriel.

A Gabriel who would chew up anyone who touched his daughter.

"You know he won't give permission," she admitted.

Her father was in charge. His rules meant that only one who could stand against him in a fight was allowed to date her.

Or anything else.

"Hey?"

She looked at the Hound.

"If you weren't *his* daughter, I'd risk it, but crossing Gabe isn't something I'm going to do."

Ani sighed, not in disappointment, but at the futility of ever getting a different answer. "I know."

"Convince him that you're not going to get broken by a little fun, and I'll be in front of the line. Promise." The Hound leaned forward to drop a quick kiss on her lips.

It was no more than a second of affection, but he was ripped away and hurled across the aisle toward the opposite stall. The thud of his body hitting the wooden slats covered most of the curses he was yelling.

"Don't touch my pup." Gabriel stood in the middle of the aisle. He was grinning, but his posture was one of menace. Of course, he was the Hound that controlled the Wild Hunt, so menace was as natural as breathing for him.

The Hound on the floor felt the back of his head as he

leaned on one partition of the wooden stall. "Damn, Gabriel. I didn't touch her."

"Your lips were on hers. That's *touching*," Gabriel growled.

Ani stepped in front of her father and poked him in the chest. "Don't act like it's wrong for them to respond to me."

He glared at her but didn't lift a hand. "I am the Gabriel. I run this pack, and if any of them"—he looked past her to the Hound on the floor—"want to challenge me over you, all they need to do is say the word."

The Hound on the floor spoke up. "I turned her down."

"Not because she lacks anything," Gabriel growled.

"No, no." The Hound held up his hands. "She's perfect, Gabe . . . but you said she was off-limits."

Gabriel held a hand out to the Hound on the floor without looking at him.

The Hound glanced at her. "Sorry . . . I, umm, touched you."

Ani rolled her eyes. "You're a peach."

"Sorry, Gabriel. It won't happen again." The Hound straddled his bike and left with a roar that was more growl than a real Harley's engine could mimic.

For a heartbeat, it was perfectly quiet in the stable. The steeds stayed silent and motionless.

"My perfect pup." Gabriel stepped up and ruffled her hair. "He doesn't deserve you. None of them do."

She shoved him away. "So, you'd rather I'm skin starved?"

5

Gabriel snorted. "You're not starved."

"I would be if I followed all of your rules," she muttered.

"And I wouldn't have so many rules if I thought you'd follow them all." He threw a punch, which she dodged. It was nice, but not backed by the full force of his strength or weight. He always held back. *That* was insulting. If she were truly a part of the Hunt, he'd fight with her the way he fought with all the rest. He'd train her. *He'd accept me in the pack.*

"You suck at fatherhood, Gabe." She turned away and started down the aisle.

He couldn't taste her feelings, not like the most of the Dark Court. Hounds weren't nourished on the same things, so her emotions were hidden to them. The peculiarity of the Hunt's inability to taste emotions while everyone around them could made them very blunt in their own expressions. It worked out well: Dark Court faeries were nourished by swallowing dark emotions; Hounds required physical touch for sustenance. So the Hunt caused the fear and terror that fed the court, and the court provided the touch the Hounds required. Ani was abnormal in that she needed both.

Which sucks.

"Ani?"

She didn't stop walking. There was no way she was going to let him see the tears building in her eyes. *Just another proof of my weakness.* She gestured over her shoulder. "I get it, *Daddy.* I'm not welcome."

"Ani."

Tears leaked onto her cheeks as she stopped in the doorway, but she didn't turn back.

"Promise to follow the rules while we're out, and you could probably borrow Che's steed again tonight." His voice held the hope he wouldn't say aloud. "*If* she agrees."

Ani turned then and smiled at him. "Yeah?"

"Yeah." He didn't move, didn't comment on the tears on her cheeks, but his voice softened and he added, "And I'm *not* an awful father."

"Maybe."

"I just don't want to think about you wanting . . . things . . . or getting hurt." Gabriel folded the cloth that the Hound had dropped, looking at it rather than at her. "Irial says you're okay though. I ask. I do try."

"I know." She shook her hair back and struggled to be reasonable. That was the worst part sometimes; she *did* know that Gabriel tried. She knew he trusted Irial's judgment, trusted Chela, trusted his pack. He'd never raised a daughter—these past few months that he'd had her around were the sum total of his father-daughter parenting experience. But, she'd never had pack hungers before either. It was a new experience all around.

Later, after she'd secured Chela's consent, gone over the regular stay-close-to-Gabriel rules, and promised to stick with the pack, Ani was back in the stable with her father.

"If Che's steed has anything to say, it'll tell me, and I'll tell you." Gabriel's reminder that she couldn't hear Chela's steed—*that I'll never hear one*—was delivered with an ominous rumble in his voice. He was already feeling the heightened connection to the Hounds who were filling the aisles.

Somewhere in the distance, a howl rose like the scream of wind. Ani knew that only the Hunt heard it, but both mortal and faery *felt* it in the shivers that raced over suddenly chilled skin. To some, it was as if sirens came toward them, as if ambulances and police sped to them carrying words of sudden deaths or horrific accidents.

The Wild Hunt rides.

As Ani looked over the assembling Hounds, the green of their eyes and the clouds of their breath were clear. Wolves filled the room where the steeds were not. They would run between the hooves of the steeds, a roil of fur and teeth. Steed and wolf all waited for their Gabriel's word to begin, to run, to chase those foolish enough to attract their attention. Terror built and filled the air with a prestorm charge. Those not belonging to the Hunt would have to struggle to breathe. Mortals on the nearby streets would cringe, scurry into their dens, or turn into other alleys. If they stayed, they'd not see the true face of the Hunt, but explain it away—*earthquake?*

trains? storms? street fights?—with the willful ignorance
mortals clung to so fiercely. They didn't often stay; they ran.
It was the order of things: prey runs, and predators pursue.

Her father, her Gabriel, strode through the room assess-
ing them.

Ani felt the stroke of icy fingers on her skin as they
prepared to ride. She bit down on her lip to keep from
urging her father to sound the call. Her knuckles whitened
as she clenched the edge of the wooden wall beside her. She
looked at their horrible beauty and shivered.

If they were mine . . . I'd belong.

Then Gabriel was beside her.

"You are my pup, Ani." Gabriel cupped her cheek in his
massive hand. "To be worthy of you, any Hound would have
to be willing to face me. He'd need to be strong enough to
lead them."

"*I* want to lead them," she whispered. "I want to be their
Gabrielle."

"You're too mortal to hold control of them." Gabriel's
eyes were monstrous. His skin was the touch of terror, of
death, of nightmares that were Un-Named. "And too much
mine to not be with the Hunt. I'm sorry."

She held his gaze. Something feral inside of her under-
stood that this was why she couldn't live with Rabbit: her
brother wasn't as fierce as her father was. Tish wasn't. Ani
desperately wanted to be. Like the rest of the Hounds

mounting their steeds, Ani knew that Gabriel could kill her if she disobeyed. It was a restraint she needed: it kept her closer to following rules.

"I can't take the Hunt from you"—she flashed her teeth at her father—"yet. Maybe I'll surprise you."

"Makes me proud that you want to," he said.

For a moment, the pride in her father's eyes was the sum of her world. She belonged. For tonight, she was included in the pack. He made it so.

If only I always was.

But there were no unclaimed steeds, and her mortal blood meant she'd never be strong enough to become Gabriel's successor, never be truly Pack.

A taste of belonging . . .

It wasn't enough, not truly, but it was something.

Then a howl unlike anything else in this world or the next came to his lips, and the rest of the pack echoed it. *She* echoed it.

Gabriel tossed her atop Chela's steed and growled, "We ride."